NorthParadePublishing

©2014 North Parade Publishing Ltd.
4 North Parade,
Bath BA1 1LF. UK
www.nppbooks.co.uk

Sing Along Songs

This book belongs to

....

The Wheels on the Bus

The wheels
on the bus go
round and round,
Round and round,
Round and round.
The wheels on the bus go
round and round, all day long.

The wipers on the bus go swish swish swish,
Swish swish swish,
Swish swish swish.
The wipers on the bus go swish swish swish,
All day long.

The horn on the bus goes beep beep beep,
Beep beep beep,
beep beep beep.
The horn on the bus goes beep beep beep,
All day long.

The children on the bus go up and down,
Up and down,
Up and down.
The children on the bus go up and down,
All day long.

The babies on the bus go
"Wah wah wah,
Wah wah wah,
Wah wah wah".
The babies on the bus go
"Wah wah wah",
All day long.

The mums on the bus go "Sshh sshh sshh,
Sshh sshh sshh,
Sshh sshh sshh".
The mums on the bus go "Sshh sshh sshh",
All day long.

The driver on the bus says
"Move on back,
Move on back,
Move on back".
The driver on the bus says
"Move on back",
All day long.

The wheels on the bus go
Round and round,
Round and round,
Round and round.
The wheels on the bus
go round and round,
All day long.

Row Row Row Your Boat

Row row row your boat,
gently down the stream,
merrily, merrily, merrily, merrily,
life is but a dream....

If You're Happy And You Know It!

If you're happy and you know it, clap your hands!
If you're happy and you know it, clap your hands!
If you're happy and you know it,
And you really want to show it,
If you're happy and you know it, clap your hands!

If you're happy and you know it, stomp your feet!
If you're happy and you know it, stomp your feet!
If you're happy and you know it,
And you really want to show it,
If you're happy and you know it, stomp your feet!

If you're happy and you know it, jump up!
If you're happy and you know it, jump up!
If you're happy and you know it,
And you really want to show it,
If you're happy and you know it, jump up!

If you're happy and you know it, shout "We are!".
If you're happy and you know it, shout "We are!".
If you're happy and you know it,
And you really want to show it,
If you're happy and you know it,
shout "We are!".

Old MacDonald

Old MacDonald had a farm, E-I-E-I-O

And on his farm he had a **COW**, E-I-E-I-O
With a moo, moo here and a moo, moo there,
Here a moo, there a moo,
Everywhere a moo-moo,
Old MacDonald had a farm, E-I-E-I-O.

Old MacDonald had a farm, E-I-E-I-O

And on his farm he had a **pig**, E-I-E-I-O
With an oink, oink here and an oink, oink there
Here an oink, there an oink,
Everywhere an oink-oink;
Moo-moo here and a moo-moo there,
Here a moo, there a moo,
Everywhere a moo-moo,
Old MacDonald had a farm, E-I-E-I-O.

Old MacDonald had a farm, E-I-E-I-O

And on his farm he had a **horse**, E-I-E-I-O

With a neigh, neigh here and a neigh, neigh there
Here a neigh, there a neigh,
Everywhere a neigh, neigh;

Oink, oink here and an oink, oink there
Here an oink, there an oink,
Everywhere an oink-oink;

Moo-moo here and a moo-moo there,
Here a moo, there a moo,
Everywhere a moo-moo,

Old MacDonald had a farm,
E-I-E-I-O.

She'll Be Coming Round The Mountain

She'll be coming 'round the mountain when she comes,
She'll be coming 'round the mountain when she comes,
She'll be coming 'round the mountain,
Coming 'round the mountain,
Coming 'round the mountain when she comes.

She'll be riding six white horses when she comes,
She'll be riding six white horses when she comes,
She'll be riding six white horses,
Riding six white horses,
Riding six white horses when she comes.

And we'll all go out to meet her when she comes,
And we'll all go out to meet her when she comes,
And we'll all go out to meet her,
All go out to meet her,
All go out to meet her when she comes.

She'll be wearing pink pyjamas when she comes,
She'll be wearing pink pyjamas when she comes,
She'll be wearing pink pyjamas,
Wearing pink pyjamas,
Wearing pink pyjamas when she comes.

We'll be singing Hallelujah when she comes,
We'll be singing Hallelujah when she comes,
We'll be singing Hallelujah,
Singing Hallelujah,
Singing Hallelujah when she comes.

Do Your Ears Hang Low?

Do your ears hang low?
Do they wobble to and fro?
Can you tie them in a knot?
Can you tie them in a bow?
Can you throw them o'er your shoulder
Like a regimental soldier?

Do your ears hang low?

Do your ears hang high?
Do they reach up to the sky?
Do they droop when they are wet?
Do they stiffen when they're dry?
Can you semaphore your neighbour
With the minimum of labour?

Do your ears hang high?

Do your ears **flip-flop?**
Can you use them for a mop?
Are they stringy at the bottom?
Are they curly at the top?
Can you use them for a swatter?
Can you use them for a blotter?

Do your ears **flip-flop?**

Do your ears **hang out?**
Can you waggle them about?
Can you flip them up and down?
As you fly around the town?
Can you shut them up for sure
When you hear an awful bore?

Do your ears **hang out?**

tsy Bitsy Spider

The itsy bitsy
spider,
Went up the water spout.

Down came the rain,
And washed the
spider out.

Out came the sun,
And dried up all the rain

And the itsy bitsy
spider
Went up the spout again.

London Bridge

London Bridge is falling down,
Falling down, falling down.
London Bridge is falling down,
My fair lady!

Build it up with **iron and steel**,
Iron and steel, iron and steel.
Build it up with iron and steel,
My fair lady!

Iron and steel will bend and bow,
Bend and bow, bend and bow.
Iron and steel will bend and bow,
My fair lady!

Here's a prisoner I have caught,
I have caught, I have caught.
Here's a prisoner I have caught,
My fair lady!

Off to prison he must go,
He must go, he must go.
Off to prison he must go,
My fair lady!